M000105001

presents

HAPPY

This edition published by Parragon Books Ltd in 2015

Parragon Books Ltd
Chartist House
15–17 Trim Street
Bath BA1 1HA, UK
www.parragon.com

Copyright © Parragon Books Ltd 2015

Written and illustrated by Emily Portnoi
Edited by Frances Prior-Reeves

All rights reserved. No part of this publication may be
reproduced, stored in a retrieval system or transmitted,
in any form or by any means, electronic, mechanical,
photocopying, recording or otherwise, without the prior
permission of the copyright holder.

ISBN 978-1-4748-0427-1

Printed in China

Moodles

presents

HAPPY

MOODLE YOUR WAY TO A SMILE

PaRragon

Bath · New York · Cologne · Melbourne · Delhi
Hong Kong · Shenzhen · Singapore · Amsterdam

WELCOME
to your moodle book.

'What is a moodle?' I hear you ask. Well, a moodle is just a doodle with the power to change your mood. Be it happy to sad, sad to mad or mad back to glad. Cheaper than therapy, quicker than chanting chakras, tastier than a cabbage leaf and sandpaper detox, and less fattening than chocolate cake!

The moodle: a simple thing that can really turn your day around.

All you need is a pen or pencil, imagination and an open mind. Be prepared to delve into your innermost thoughts, ideas and concepts. Uncover your subconscious and lay it bare on the page — admire it, mock it and marvel at it until you feel altogether much chirpier. Let the moodle wisdom penetrate your subconscious and guide you on a magical mental journey; follow the line you create until the final stop — happiness!

There's nothing like a **spot of retail therapy** to lift the spirits.

Moodle your **guilt-free** purchases.

FANCY A COOL NEW HAIRDO?

Try out a different style on each of these heads.

YOU'RE THE STAR!

Sketch yourself in a favourite TV or movie scene.

DECORATE YOUR DOUGHNUTS.

Turn this scribble into your own **MONSTER** friends.

Moodle a FLAMBOYANCE of flamingos.

Want to be treated like a national treasure?

Draw **your face** on this stamp.

Draw yourself jumping impossibly high.

You've done **very well** for yourself, and look: now you have your very own private jet!

Draw yourself, family and friends on board, cut out, fold and then fly to an island paradise.

HOW TO MAKE YOUR AEROPLANE

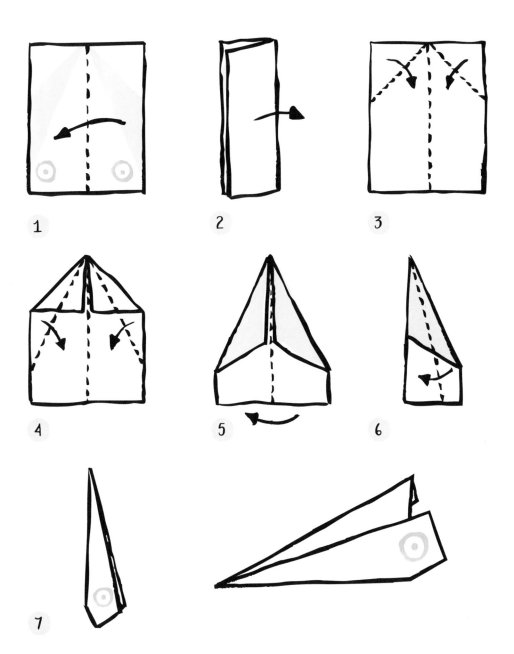

Take the largest note from your wallet. Hide it. Draw a treasure map.

Wait 7 months, 4 days and 3 hours. Then follow the map to discover precious money. (OOOH HURRAH, ME HEARTIES!)

Save all the BEST compliments you receive.

YOU'RE MAGIC!

What can you make appear out of the hat?

Moodle the impossible.

Sketch your **HAPPY PLACE,**
then escape there whenever you need to —
cheaper than a package holiday.

STOP PROCRASTINATING.

JUST DRAW SOMETHING!

(You've got 15 seconds from now.)

Finishing a puzzle can be **very satisfying.** With this puzzle all you have to do is draw the finished picture, make it as complicated as you like, then sit back, admire and feel smug.

Cover the entire page in grey scribbled pencil.
Then use an eraser to draw a bright sunshine.

GET FOCUSED!

Draw your ambition here, then take aim.

Moodle your happiest memories on this album page.

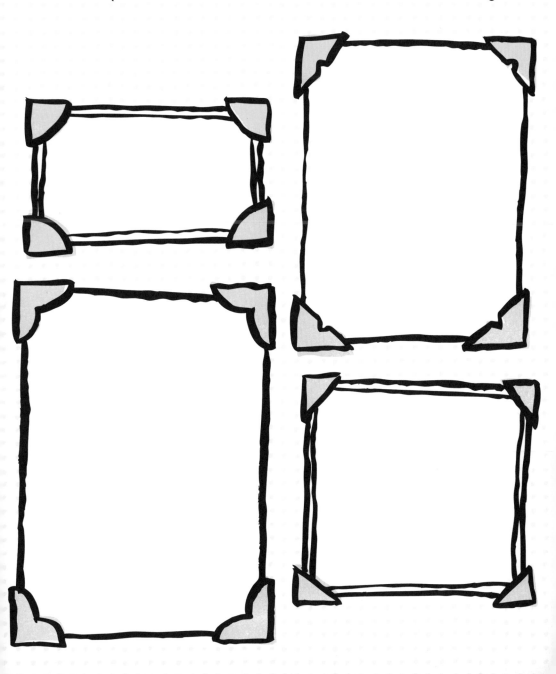

Enjoy the **little things.**

Draw five things smaller than your thumbnail.

Stop and smell the roses.

Draw a MASSIVE grin on this face.

Cut along the dotted lines and wear as a mask!

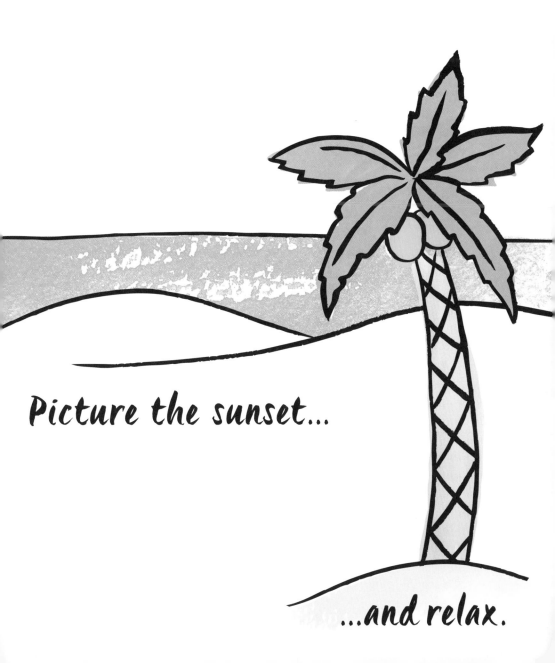

Picture the sunset...

...and relax.

DRAW THE HOUSE OF YOUR DREAMS: THE HOUSE YOU DESERVE.

Comfort food!
Moodle your favourite dish.

Mmm!

TELL THE STORY OF YOUR GREATEST ADVENTURE
in moodles.

Draw four BEAUTIFUL things you've seen today.

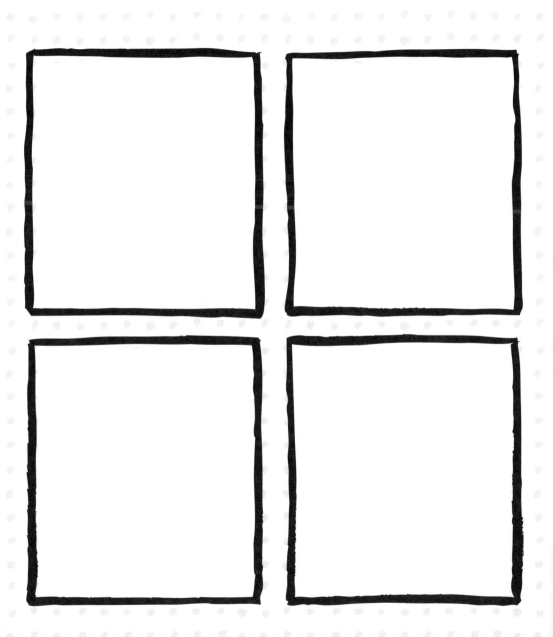

Moodle the cover of your autobiography.

The key to success is
the ability to choose a path and stick to it.

Draw a picture without taking your pen off of the page.

DRAW YOURSELF DANCING.

Write yourself a LOVE LETTER with your left hand.

(Or your right if you're left-handed — stop being difficult!)

PARTY TIME!

Moodle some bright, cheery decorations.

COLOUR IN this picture.
Colour over the lines if it
makes you happier!

Laughter is the key to happiness.

Draw the last thing that made you laugh.

Join the dots in any order you like —
there is no right or wrong answer.

Keep going until you have your
own wonderful, unique design.

QUICK DRAW.

Draw the first thing you think
of when you read these words:

GALLOP

ADVENTURE

TWISTED

TAG THIS WALL.

Moodle an amazing firework display.

Oooh, Aaah!

Design a **hippy's happy** T-shirt.

Draw a grumpy you on this page.
And a happy you on the next right-hand page.

Then flick this page back and forth.

Design your own coat of arms and
DISPLAY IT WITH PRIDE.

Did it make you smile?

BECOME SELF-AWARE.

Draw what you can taste, smell and feel.

Moodle your GREATEST achievement.

Pete the unicorn has gone to Awesome Happy World. Can you create his holiday postcard?

YOUR FAMILY AND FRIENDS ARE HIDDEN TREASURES.

Draw their faces on these coins and enjoy their riches.

Moodle this penguin its soulmate.

Exercise is the KEY to happiness.

Take this book for a short, fast walk, then chart your journey on this page.

Sketch YOUR DOOR for opportunity to knock on.

Draw a shrine to the thing or person you love most.
(Try not to enter creepy stalker territory!)

MAGNIFY YOUR HAPPINESS.

Draw your smile through this magnifying glass.

Moodle yourself as an ADORABLE kitten.

Moodle the song in your heart.

Since you are **truly super-duper,**
you should have a sidekick.

Moodle your **ultimate awesome** sidekick.

REACH FOR THE STARS.

Draw THREE THINGS
you are grateful for today.

Fill your cup with moodles.
(So it runneth over.)

WANTED

★

★

MY JOY

Description:

Last seen:

DRAW SOME NEW LOGO DESIGNS
FOR HAPPY CORP.

Moodle a pyramid of snails.

Set all the clocks
to Sunday morning...

...and snooze.

According to Zen philosophy, the key to inner happiness is to **consider things from every angle.** Pick an object and draw it from the top, bottom, right and left.

A tortoise's shell is his CASTLE.

Give each of these tortoises their own unique and wonderful shell design.

Write a coded message using only moodles. Show it to a
clever clogs friend, to see if he or she can crack your code.

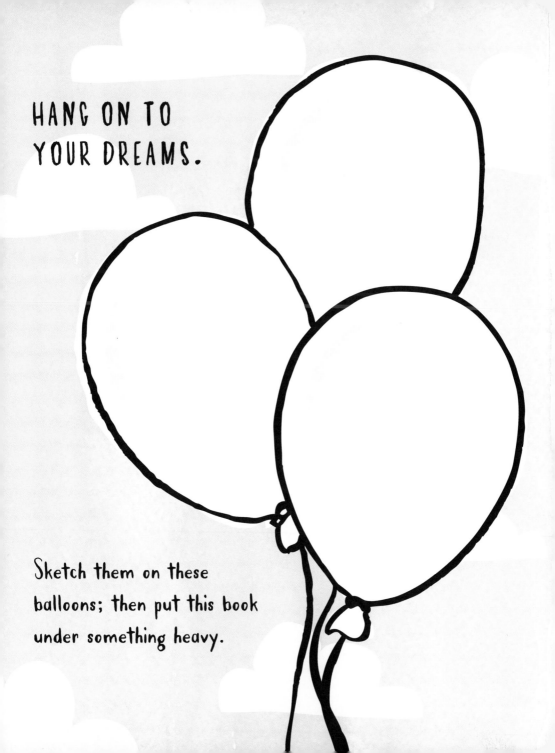

HANG ON TO YOUR DREAMS.

Sketch them on these balloons; then put this book under something heavy.

Design some fancy face topiary to make you smile.

Moodle your message in a bottle.
Then let it set sail on the high
seas of *chance and fate.*

PRACTISE YOUR SMILES.

Moodle them here.

Smirk

Grin

Beam

Pout

Coy

Excited

Happy

Surprised

Cheeky

Mischievous

A wise man once said,
'Count your age by friends, not years.'

Moodle all your friends as candles on your cake.

Supplement your life.

Moodle little happy faces on each of these multivitamins.

Moodle your name **REALLY** enthusiastically.

Draw around your toes and then
moodle them into a family of piggies.

Moodle the faces these **funny noses** belong to.

GET THE MOST OUT OF LIFE.
Moodle on this page until there
isn't a speck of white showing.

Moodle yourself as a SUPERSTAR.

Hide 20 miniature grinning
frogs on other pages of this book.

TRAVEL BROADENS THE MIND.
Moodle ...

...on the toilet.

- -

...at the foot of your bed.

...at the top of the stairs.

...on your doorstep.

Nothing beats a home-made meal to warm your soul.
WHAT ARE **YOU** COOKING?

Cheer up this old deer.

Moodle in the rest of her body.

Moodle your favourite view,
so that you can take some time to enjoy the
view whenever you have a spare minute.

YOU'RE A SUPER HUMAN!

How much can you balance
on your little finger?

SURPRISE! Here's a little present for you.

Moodle your own surprise gift. Then act surprised.

Start an appreciation
society for...

MOODLE THE SUN COMING OUT.

MOODLE A
RAINBOW.

This poor polar bear has CHILLY TOES.
Moodle him some woolly socks.

AND THE WINNER IS...

Write your winner's acceptance speech.

All moodles complete and wisdom absorbed, you will by now have reached a state of complete and utter happiness. You may well be floating on a higher mental plane, radiating love, Zen and light. And if you ever come down again, simply revisit the pages of this book to top up your happiness.